Multiply your Maths skills with CGP!

This brilliant CGP book is the best way to help pupils master KS2 Multiplication and Division for the Maths SATs.

It's packed with bite-sized 10-Minute Tests that become tougher as pupils build up their skills. They're great prep for both the Arithmetic and Reasoning parts of the SATs.

We've even included full answers to every question — plus a handy chart to check progress too!

What CGP is all about

Our sole aim here at CGP is to produce the highest quality books — carefully written, immaculately presented and dangerously close to being funny.

Then we work our socks off to get them out to you — at the cheapest possible prices.

Published by CGP

Editors: Michael Bushell, Sarah George and Tom Miles

With thanks to Amanda MacNaughton for the reviewing.
With thanks to David Ryan for the proofreading.

ISBN: 978 1 78908 451 1

Clipart from Corel®
Printed by Elanders Ltd, Newcastle upon Tyne.

Based on the classic CGP style created by Richard Parsons.

Contents

Test 1 2

Test 2 4

Test 3 6

Test 4 8

Test 5 10

Test 6 12

Test 7 14

Test 8 16

Test 9 18

Test 10 20

Test 11 22

Test 12 24

Answers 26

How to Use this Book

- This book contains <u>12 tests</u>, all geared towards improving your multiplication and division skills.

- Each test is out of <u>12 marks</u> and should take about <u>10 minutes</u> to complete.

- Each test starts with some <u>warm-up questions</u> to get you going and ends with a <u>problem solving question</u>.

- The tests <u>increase in difficulty</u> as you go through the book.

- <u>Answers</u> and a <u>Progress Chart</u> can be found at the <u>back</u> of the book.

Test 1

Warm up

1. Use your times tables to answer these questions.

   a) 3 × 5 = ...

   b) 2 × 7 = ...

   c) 4 × 4 = ...

   d) 6 × 5 = ...

   _____
   2 marks

2. a) Circle all the numbers that are multiples of 3.

   6   13   16   21   23   24

   _____
   1 mark

   a) Circle all the numbers that are multiples of 8.

   4   10   24   36   48   72

   _____
   1 mark

3. Work out the answers to these calculations.

   ```
       1 8              2 3              3 4
   ×     2          ×     6          ×     3
   _____          _____          _____

   ............      ............      ............
   _____          _____          _____
   ```
   _____
   2 marks

4. Work out:

   4 × 10 = ...   40 × 10 = ...

   40 × 100 = ...   40 × 1000 = ...

   _____
   2 marks

5. What is 199 × 3?

....
<u>1 mark</u>

6. Nathan is entering a fun run to raise money for charity. He is sponsored by 7 of his friends who each pledge to donate £5 for every mile that he completes.

Nathan runs for 10 miles.

Complete the calculation below.

□ friends × £□ × □ miles = □ × □ = £□
<u>1 mark</u>

Nathan also has sponsorship from Sixudder Farm. They offer to donate £13 for each of the first five miles and three times as much for each mile after that.

How much money will Sixudder Farm donate?

Show your working.

£ ....
<u>2 marks</u>

END OF TEST

/ 12

Warm up

1. Use your times tables to calculate:

   a) $5 \times 6 =$ ....

   b) $4 \times 8 =$ ....

   c) $3 \times 9 =$ ....

   d) $7 \times 7 =$ ....

   2 marks

2. Work out the answer to each of these calculations.

   a) $2 \times 10 =$ ....

   b) $8 \times 100 =$ ....

   1 mark

3. Work out:

   $4.5 \times 10 =$ ....

   $1.1 \times 10 =$ ....

   $6.7 \times 100 =$ ....

   $0.2 \times 1000 =$ ....

   2 marks

4. Work out the answers to these calculations.

   $$\begin{array}{r} 2 \ 1 \ 3 \\ \times \quad\quad 7 \\ \hline \\ \text{...................} \\ \hline \end{array}$$

   $$\begin{array}{r} 3 \ 4 \ 1 \\ \times \quad\quad 6 \\ \hline \\ \text{...................} \\ \hline \end{array}$$

   2 marks

5. What is five hundred and sixty-three multiplied by five?

....
1 mark

6. Mary is a sailing instructor at Leaky Boat Lodge.
Each day, she teaches a morning beginner class costing £13
and an afternoon expert class costing £25.

How much money can Mary earn in 7 days?

£....................
2 marks

There is also a pirate adventure package costing £75.
Mary sells 6 of them over the year. She earns £402 for these
and thinks she must have undercharged someone.

How much money is she missing?

£....................
2 marks

END OF TEST

/ 12

Warm up

1. Fill in the boxes to complete these calculations.

   a) 5 × ☐ = 10   b) 2 × ☐ = 10

   c) 2 × ☐ = 12   d) 3 × ☐ = 12

   _____
   2 marks

2. Use your times tables to solve these calculations.

   a) 14 ÷ 2 = ...   b) 20 ÷ 5 = ...

   c) 24 ÷ 4 = ...   d) 30 ÷ 6 = ...

   _____
   2 marks

3. Work out:

   520 ÷ 10 = ...   400 ÷ 10 = ...

   8800 ÷ 100 = ...   95 000 ÷ 1000 = ...

   _____
   2 marks

4. Work out the answer to these calculations.

   ....
   4 | 7 2   6 | 9 6   3 | 8 4

   _____
   2 marks

5.   Tens United win the Division Cup. To celebrate, they give away a free scarf to 1 out of every 10 fans who attend their next match.

If 800 fans attend the next match, how many will get a free scarf?

.... fans

6.   Fareed needs to herd four goats across a rickety bridge.
The bridge can safely take a total weight of up to 595 kg.

The four goats all weigh the same as each other.
Fareed weighs 75 kg.

What is the maximum possible weight that each goat can be?

Show your working.

.... kg

END OF TEST

/ 12

Warm up

1. Use your times tables to solve these calculations.

    a) 28 ÷ 4 = ...

    b) 36 ÷ 6 = ...

    c) 40 ÷ 5 = ...

    d) 54 ÷ 9 = ...

    _____
    2 marks

2. Work out the answer to each of these calculations.

    a) 30 ÷ 10 = ...

    b) 500 ÷ 10 = ...

    c) 640 ÷ 10 = ...

    d) 2000 ÷ 100 = ...

    _____
    2 marks

3. Draw lines to match each calculation with its answer.

    | 5.6 ÷ 100 | 56 ÷ 100 | 5600 ÷ 100 | 560 ÷ 100 |

    | 56 | 0.56 | 5.6 | 0.056 |

    _____
    1 mark

4. Work out the answer to these calculations.

    .... remainder: ......

    3 | 7 4

    .... remainder: ......

    5 | 8 4

    _____
    2 marks

5. The distance around the edge of a lake is 2034 m.
    Jenna runs around the lake six times.

    How far does Jenna run in total?

    .... m   ———
                                       1 mark

6. Taylor and Frank are taking their three children on holiday.
    They find a package holiday that costs £3645 in total.

    How much does this holiday cost per person?

    £ ....   ———
                             2 marks

    A second package holiday costs £900 per person,
    but they get a discount of £250 off the total cost.

    What is the difference in price between the two holidays?

    £ ....   ———
                             2 marks

END OF TEST

/ 12

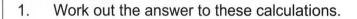

Warm up

1.   Work out the answer to these calculations.

   a) 9 × 4 = ...   b) 27 ÷ 3 = ...

   c) 8 × 8 = ...   d) 40 ÷ 8 = ...

   _____
   2 marks

2.   a) What is five lots of sixteen?   b) What is seven lots of twelve?

                    ....   _____
                                                                           1 mark

3.   Work out:

   Forty-six multiplied by one thousand

                                        ....   _____
                                                                    1 mark

   Twenty-five thousand divided by one hundred

                                        ....   _____
                                                                    1 mark

4.   Work out the answers to these calculations.

```
      1  5  2  3                 1  2  4  7
   ×           4              ×           7
   _____               _____

   ..................         ..................
   _____               _____
```
   _____
   2 marks

5. Fill in the boxes to complete these calculations.

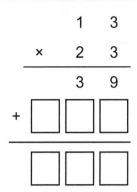

```
        1   3                      2   1
    ×   2   3                  ×   2   4
    ─────────                  ─────────
        3   9                     □   □
  + □  □  □                  + 4   2   0
  ─────────                  ─────────
    □  □  □                    □   □   □
```

2 marks

7. Sasha spends £50 on tickets at a fun fair.
She goes on the carousel twice.

How many times does she ride the roller coaster?

Ticket Prices

Carousel   £7

Roller Coaster   £9

.... times

2 marks

END OF TEST

/ 12

Test 6

Warm up

1. Work out the answer to these calculations.

    a) 9 × 6 = ...

    b) 42 ÷ 7 = ...

    c) 7 × 9 = ...

    d) 81 ÷ 9 = ...

    _____
    2 marks

2. Work out the answer to these calculations.

    a) 10 × 50 = ...

    b) 7 × 1000 = ...

    c) 80 ÷ 100 = ...

    d) 2000 ÷ 10 = ...

    _____
    2 marks

3. Write in the missing digits to make these calculations correct.

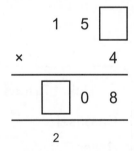

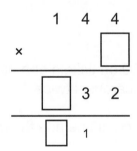

_____
2 marks

4. Circle all the calculations below that have a remainder of 0.

   18 ÷ 4   21 ÷ 3   19 ÷ 6   42 ÷ 7

            42 ÷ 6   26 ÷ 8   33 ÷ 3   46 ÷ 9

_____
1 mark

12

5. Gordon has calculated 4 × 255.
   He's showing off his working on the right.

   Use Gordon's answer to work out:

   40 × 255 = ...

   4 × 25 500 = ...

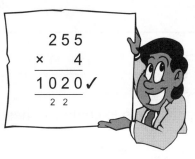

$$\begin{array}{r} 255 \\ \times\quad 4 \\ \hline 1020 \checkmark \\ \scriptstyle 2\ 2 \end{array}$$

   _____
   2 marks

6. Habiba shares a box of 51 chocolates evenly between her
   four children and takes the left over chocolates for herself.

   How many chocolates does Habiba get?

   .... chocolates
   _____
   1 mark

7. Claire drives into town and pays £5 to park her car.
   She then buys four identical rugs and a can of carpet cleaner.

   Claire spends £264 in total and each rug
   costs a whole number of pounds.

   What is the lowest possible
   price of the carpet cleaner?

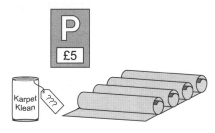

   £ ....
   _____
   2 marks

END OF TEST

/ 12

Test 6

10

Warm up

1. Fill in the gaps to complete these calculations.

   a) 5 × .... = 10

   b) 3 × .... = 18

   c) .... × 7 = 28

   d) .... × 9 = 9

   _____
   2 marks

2. Fill in the gaps to complete these calculations.

   a) 25 ÷ .... = 5

   b) 63 ÷ .... = 9

   c) .... ÷ 4 = 8

   d) .... ÷ 9 = 3

   _____
   2 marks

3. A toaster takes 3 minutes to toast bread.
   It can hold 2 slices of bread at the same time.

   How many slices of bread can be toasted in 84 minutes?

   .... slices   _____
   2 marks

4. Work out the answer to these calculations.

   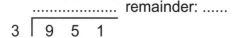

   .... remainder: .... remainder: ......

   3 | 9 5 1   6 | 4 5 3

   _____
   2 marks

Test 7
14

5. Work out:

```
    9 5 8 3              5 8 2 3
  ×       6            ×       9
  _____            _____

  ...............      ...............
  _____            _____
```

6. Milk from Sixudder Farm is sold in small and large bottles.
    The large bottles have the following label.

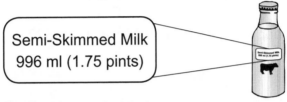

    Semi-Skimmed Milk
    996 ml (1.75 pints)

    A large bottle holds 4 times as much as a small bottle.

    How many ml of milk does a small bottle hold?

    .... ml

    On a good day, the farm produces 2000 large bottles of milk.

    How many pints of milk is this?

    .... pints

END OF TEST

/ 12

Warm up

1. Fill in the gaps with 10, 100 or 1000 to complete these calculations.

   a) 289 × .... = 2890

   b) 517 × .... = 51 700

   c) 4600 ÷ .... = 46

   d) 72 500 ÷ .... = 72.5

   _____
   2 marks

2. a) What do you need to multiply 17 by to get 170?

   ....

   b) What number when divided by 10 results in 52?

   ....
   _____
   1 mark

3. Work out:

	3	4
×	1	3

	4	2
×	2	9

   _____
   2 marks

4. Work out:

   .... remainder: ......

   4 | 3 6 5 2

   .... remainder: ......

   6 | 8 2 0 4

   _____
   2 marks

16

5. For each statement below, do a calculation to work out whether it is true or false and then tick the correct box.

You can divide 948 by 6 exactly.

True ☐ False ☐ _____
1 mark

534 is a multiple of 7.

True ☐ False ☐ _____
1 mark

6. A farmer plants carrots in a field.
There are 24 rows and 36 carrots in each row.

How many carrots did the farmer plant?

.... carrots _____
1 mark

The farmer has 948 beetroots.
Customers can order them in packs of 5.

How many packs can the farmer sell?

.... packs _____
2 marks

END OF TEST

/ 12

Warm up

1. a) Circle all the multiples of 12:   26   36   48   62   78

    b) Circle all the multiples of 15:   13   45   39   60   55   _____
                                                                             2 marks

2. Fill in the gaps to complete these calculations.

    a) $3 \times$ .... = 30   b) .... $\times 30 = 900$

    c) .... $\times 20 = 0$ d) $7 \times$ .... = 4900   _____
                                                                             2 marks

3. Find the remainder when:

    2986 is divided by 3   3459 is divided by 4

            Remainder: ....   Remainder: ....   _____
                                                                    2 marks

4. Work out:

    $33 \div 13$

                          .... remainder ....

    $45 \div 18$

                          .... remainder ....

    $79 \div 24$

                          .... remainder ....   _____
                                                               2 marks

5. What is:

Sixty-seven multiplied by thirty-two?

.... ‾‾‾‾‾‾‾
1 mark

Fifty-eight lots of ninety-six?

.... ‾‾‾‾‾‾‾
1 mark

6. John is planning a party. He buys 25 balloons that cost 74p each and pays with a £20 note.

How much does John get in change?

£ .... ‾‾‾‾‾‾‾
2 marks

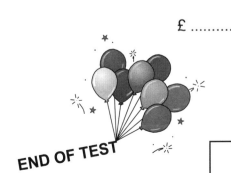

END OF TEST

/ 12

Warm up

1. Work out the answer to these calculations.

   a) 0.5 × 10 = ...

   b) 0.6 × 1000 = ...

   c) 24 ÷ 100 = ...

   d) 7 ÷ 1000 = ...

   _____
   2 marks

2. Work out the answer to these calculations.

   a) 2 × 5 ÷ 10 = ...

   b) 5 × 8 ÷ 10 = ...

   c) 3.5 × 10 ÷ 5 = ...

   d) 0.8 × 10 ÷ 2 = ...

   _____
   2 marks

3. Work out:

   .... remainder: ......

   1 4 | 1 5 9

   .... remainder: ......

   2 6 | 3 1 3

   _____
   2 marks

4. Wei is packing 160 apples into crates.
   Each crate holds 12 apples.

   How many crates does she need?

   .... crates

   _____
   2 marks

20

5. In a spelling bee, 128 contestants each spell 16 words in the first round. Then 64 contestants each spell 8 words in the second round.

How many words did the contestants spell altogether?

.... words

———
2 marks

6. A laptop has a rectangular screen.

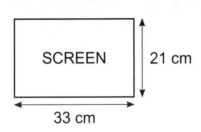

SCREEN   21 cm

33 cm

What is the area of the screen?

.... cm²

———
2 marks

END OF TEST

/ 12

Test 10

Test 11

Warm up

1. Work out the answer to these calculations.

    a) 2 × 3 × 4 = ...

    b) 3 × 5 × 2 = ...

    _____
    1 mark

2. Work out the answer to these calculations.

    a) 4 × 20 = ...

    b) 30 × 30 = ...

    c) 60 ÷ 3 = ...

    d) 500 ÷ 50 = ...

    _____
    2 marks

3. What is two hundred and thirty-eight multiplied by fifty-seven?

.... _____
2 marks

4. Work out:

    ```
        3 0 1 5
    ×       1 2
    _____
    ```

    ```
        1 6 7 4
    ×       3 1
    _____
    ```

    _____
    2 mark

5. Work out:

    ....
    12 | 2 8 0 8

    ....
    15 | 4 7 2 5

    _____
    2 marks

6. A car park has a row of 12 parking spaces.
    The width of each parking space is 360 cm.

    What is the combined width of 12 parking spaces?

    .... cm   _____
                                  1 mark

    The row of 12 spaces covers a width of 5640 cm. There are equally
    sized gaps between every two of these spaces and no gaps at the
    ends of the row. A few parking spaces have been drawn below.

    360 cm

    How wide is the gap between two parking spaces?

    .... cm   _____
                                  2 marks

    END OF TEST

    | / 12 |

1. Work out the answer to these calculations.

   a) 4^2 = ...

   b) 9^2 = ...

   c) 2^3 = ...

   d) 3^3 = ...

   _____
   2 marks

2. Fill in the gaps to complete these calculations.

   a) $30 \times$ .... $= 600$

   b) .... $\times 50 = 2000$

   c) $800 \div$ .... $= 20$

   d) $9000 \div$ .... $= 30$

   _____
   2 marks

3. Work out:

```
      9  2  1  8              7  5  4  1
   ×        3  2           ×        9  6
   _____          _____
```

   _____
   2 marks

4. A librarian wants to spread 308 books evenly across 14 shelves.

   How many books should they place on each shelf?

.... books

   _____
   1 mark

5. Calculate 5876 ÷ 13.

.... $\overline{\text{1 mark}}$

6. Mr Boar teaches a class of 24 pupils. Whenever the class reads a book, each pupil reads an equal number of words and Mr Boar reads any words that are left over.

The class reads a book that contains 9863 words.
How many words will be read by Mr Boar?

.... words $\overline{\text{2 marks}}$

The class reads a book with between 2470 and 2480 words.
Mr Boar doesn't read any of the words.

How many words does the book have?

.... words $\overline{\text{2 marks}}$

END OF TEST

/ 12

Answers

Test 1 – pages 2-3

1. a) 15 b) 14 c) 16 d) 30
   (2 marks for all four correct, otherwise 1 mark for at least two correct)
2. a) 6, 21 and 24 (**1 mark**)
   b) 24, 48 and 72 (**1 mark**)
3. $\begin{array}{r} 18 \\ \times\ \ 2 \\ \hline 36 \\ \hline {\scriptstyle 1} \end{array}$ $\quad$ $\begin{array}{r} 23 \\ \times\ \ 6 \\ \hline 138 \\ \hline {\scriptstyle 1} \end{array}$ $\quad$ $\begin{array}{r} 34 \\ \times\ \ 3 \\ \hline 102 \\ \hline {\scriptstyle 1} \end{array}$
   (2 marks for all three correct, otherwise 1 mark for at least two correct)
4. 4 × 10 = 40 $\quad$ 40 × 10 = 400
   40 × 100 = 4000 $\quad$ 40 × 1000 = 40 000
   (2 marks for all four correct, otherwise 1 mark for at least two correct)
5. 200 × 3 = 600
   So 199 × 3 = 200 – 3 = 597 (**1 mark**)
6. 7 friends × £5 × 10 miles = 35 × 10 = £350
   or 7 friends × £5 × 10 miles = 7 × 50 = £350
   (**1 mark**)
   $\begin{array}{r} 13 \\ \times\ \ 5 \\ \hline 65 \\ \hline {\scriptstyle 1} \end{array}$ $\quad$ 3 × £13 = £39 $\begin{array}{r} 39 \\ \times\ \ 5 \\ \hline 195 \\ \hline {\scriptstyle 4} \end{array}$
   So Sixudder Farm will donate £65 + £195 = £260.
   (2 marks for the correct answer, otherwise 1 mark for a correct method)

Test 2 – pages 4-5

1. a) 30 b) 32 c) 27 d) 49
   (2 marks for all four correct, otherwise 1 mark for at least two correct)
2. a) 20 b) 800
   (1 mark for both correct)
3. 4.5 × 10 = 45 $\quad$ 1.1 × 10 = 11
   6.7 × 100 = 670 $\quad$ 0.2 × 1000 = 200
   (2 marks for all four correct, otherwise 1 mark for at least two correct)
4. $\begin{array}{r} 213 \\ \times\ \ 7 \\ \hline 1491 \\ \hline {\scriptstyle 2} \end{array}$ (**1 mark**) $\quad$ $\begin{array}{r} 341 \\ \times\ \ 6 \\ \hline 2046 \\ \hline {\scriptstyle 2} \end{array}$ (**1 mark**)
5. $\begin{array}{r} 563 \\ \times\ \ 5 \\ \hline 2815 \\ \hline {\scriptstyle 3\ 1} \end{array}$ (**1 mark**)
6. £13 + £25 = £38
   $\begin{array}{r} 38 \\ \times\ \ 7 \\ \hline 266 \\ \hline {\scriptstyle 5} \end{array}$
   So Mary can earn £266.
   (2 marks for the correct answer, otherwise 1 mark for a correct method)
   $\begin{array}{r} 75 \\ \times\ \ 6 \\ \hline 450 \\ \hline {\scriptstyle 3} \end{array}$
   So Mary is missing £450 – £402 = £48.
   (2 marks for the correct answer, otherwise 1 mark for a correct method)

Test 3 – pages 6-7

1. a) 2 b) 5 c) 6 d) 4
   (2 marks for all four correct, otherwise 1 mark for at least two correct)
2. a) 7 b) 4 c) 6 d) 5
   (2 marks for all four correct, otherwise 1 mark for at least two correct)
3. 520 ÷ 10 = 52 $\quad$ 400 ÷ 10 = 40
   8800 ÷ 100 = 88 $\quad$ 95 000 ÷ 1000 = 95
   (2 marks for all four correct, otherwise 1 mark for at least two correct)
4. $\begin{array}{r} 1\ 8 \\ 4\overline{)7\,^{3}2} \end{array}$ $\quad$ $\begin{array}{r} 1\ 6 \\ 6\overline{)9\,^{3}6} \end{array}$ $\quad$ $\begin{array}{r} 2\ 8 \\ 3\overline{)8\,^{2}4} \end{array}$
   (2 marks for all three correct, otherwise 1 mark for two correct)
5. 800 ÷ 10 = 80 fans (**1 mark**)
6. 595 kg – 75 kg = 520 kg
   $\begin{array}{r} 1\ 3\ 0 \\ 4\overline{)5\ {}^{1}2\ 0} \end{array}$
   So the maximum weight of each goat is 130 kg.
   (3 marks for the correct answer, otherwise 2 marks for trying to find 520 ÷ 4 or 1 mark for a correct method with more than one error)

Test 4 – pages 8-9

1. a) 7 b) 6 c) 8 d) 6
   (2 marks for all four correct, otherwise 1 mark for at least two correct)
2. a) 3 b) 50 c) 64 d) 20
   (2 marks for all four correct, otherwise 1 mark for at least two correct)

3.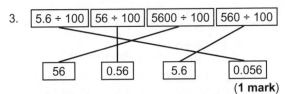

(**1 mark**)

4. $\underset{3\overline{\smash{\big)}7^14}}{2\ 4}$ remainder: 2 $\underset{5\overline{\smash{\big)}8^34}}{1\ 6}$ remainder: 4

(**1 mark for each correct calculation**)

5.
$$\begin{array}{r} 2\ 0\ 3\ 4 \\ \times\qquad 6 \\ \hline 1\ 2\ 2\ 0\ 4\ m \\ {\scriptstyle 2\ \ 2} \end{array}$$
(**1 mark**)

6.
$$\begin{array}{r} 0\ 7\ 2\ 9 \\ 5\,\overline{\smash{\big)}3\,{}^36\,{}^14\,{}^45} \end{array}$$
So the holiday costs £729 per person.
(**2 marks for the correct answer,**
otherwise 1 mark for a correct method)
$$\begin{array}{r} 9\ 0\ 0 \\ \times\quad 5 \\ \hline £\ 4\ 5\ 0\ 0 \end{array}$$
£4500 − £250 = £4250
Price difference = £4250 − £3645 = £605
(**2 marks for the correct answer,**
otherwise 1 mark for a correct method)

Test 5 – pages 10-11

1. a) 36   b) 9
   c) 64   d) 5
   (**2 marks for all four correct,**
   otherwise 1 mark for at least two correct)

2. a) 5 × 16 = 80   b) 7 × 12 = 84
   (**1 mark for both correct**)

3. 46 × 1000 = 46 000 (**1 mark**)
   25 000 ÷ 100 = 250 (**1 mark**)

4.
$$\begin{array}{r} 1\ 5\ 2\ 3 \\ \times\qquad 4 \\ \hline 6\ 0\ 9\ 2 \\ {\scriptstyle 2\ \ 1} \end{array}\qquad \begin{array}{r} 1\ 2\ 4\ 7 \\ \times\qquad 7 \\ \hline 8\ 7\ 2\ 9 \\ {\scriptstyle 1\ 3\ 4} \end{array}$$
(**1 mark for each correct answer**)

5.
$$\begin{array}{r} 1\ 3 \\ \times\ 2\ 3 \\ \hline 3\ 9 \\ +\ 2\ 6\ 0 \\ \hline 2\ 9\ 9 \end{array}$$ (**1 mark**) $$\begin{array}{r} 2\ 1 \\ \times\ 2\ 4 \\ \hline 8\ 4 \\ +\ 4\ 2\ 0 \\ \hline 5\ 0\ 4 \\ {\scriptstyle 1} \end{array}$$ (**1 mark**)

6.
$$\begin{array}{r} 3\ 2 \\ \times\ 1\ 2 \\ \hline 6\ 4 \\ +\ 3\ 2\ 0 \\ \hline 3\ 8\ 4 \end{array}$$ pieces (**1 mark**)

7. Sasha spent 2 × £7 = £14 on the carousel, so she spent £50 − £14 = £36 on the roller coaster. She rode the roller coaster 36 ÷ 9 = 4 times.
(**2 marks for the correct answer,**
otherwise 1 mark for a correct method)

Test 6 – pages 12-13

1. a) 54   b) 6   c) 63   d) 9
   (**2 marks for all four correct,**
   otherwise 1 mark for at least two correct)

2. a) 500   b) 7000   c) 0.8   d) 200
   (**2 marks for all four correct,**
   otherwise 1 mark for at least two correct)

3.
$$\begin{array}{r} 1\ 5\ 2 \\ \times\quad 4 \\ \hline 6\ 0\ 8 \\ {\scriptstyle 2} \end{array}$$ (**1 mark**) $$\begin{array}{r} 1\ 4\ 4 \\ \times\quad 3 \\ \hline 4\ 3\ 2 \\ {\scriptstyle 1\ 1} \end{array}$$ (**1 mark**)

4. 21 ÷ 3, 42 ÷ 7, 42 ÷ 6, 33 ÷ 3 (**1 mark**)

5. 40 × 255 = 10 200 (**1 mark**)
   4 × 25 500 = 102 000 (**1 mark**)

6.
$$\begin{array}{r} 1\ 2 \\ 4\,\overline{\smash{\big)}5^11} \end{array}$$ remainder 3
   So Habiba gets 3 chocolates. (**1 mark**)

7. £264 − £5 = £259
$$\begin{array}{r} 0\ 6\ 4\ r\ 3 \\ 4\,\overline{\smash{\big)}2\,{}^25\,{}^19} \end{array}$$
So the carpet cleaner was at least £3.
(**2 marks for the correct answer,**
otherwise 1 mark for a correct method)

Test 7 – pages 14-15

1. a) 2   b) 6   c) 4   d) 1
   (**2 marks for all four correct,**
   otherwise 1 mark for at least two correct)

2. a) 5   b) 7   c) 32   d) 27
   (**2 marks for all four correct,**
   otherwise 1 mark for at least two correct)

3.
$$\begin{array}{r} 2\ 8 \\ 3\,\overline{\smash{\big)}8^24} \end{array}\qquad \begin{array}{r} 2\ 8 \\ \times\quad 2 \\ \hline 5\ 6 \\ {\scriptstyle 1} \end{array}$$ So 56 slices can be toasted.
(**2 marks for the correct answer,**
otherwise 1 mark for a correct method)

4.
$$\begin{array}{r} 3\ 1\ 7 \\ 3\,\overline{\smash{\big)}9\ 5^21} \end{array}$$ remainder: 0 (**1 mark**)
$$\begin{array}{r} 0\ 7\ 5 \\ 6\,\overline{\smash{\big)}4\,{}^45\,{}^33} \end{array}$$ remainder: 3 (**1 mark**)

5.
$$\begin{array}{r} 9\ 5\ 8\ 3 \\ \times\qquad 6 \\ \hline 5\ 7\ 4\ 9\ 8 \\ {\scriptstyle 3\ 4\ 1} \end{array}$$ (**1 mark**) $$\begin{array}{r} 5\ 8\ 2\ 3 \\ \times\qquad 9 \\ \hline 5\ 2\ 4\ 0\ 7 \\ {\scriptstyle 7\ 2\ 2} \end{array}$$ (**1 mark**)

Answers

6.
$$\begin{array}{r} 2\ 4\ 9 \\ 4\overline{)9^1 9^3 6} \end{array}$$
So 249 ml (**1 mark**)

1.75 × 1000 = 1750
$$\begin{array}{r} 1\ 7\ 5\ 0 \\ \times\quad\quad 2 \\ \hline 3\ 5\ 0\ 0 \\ \scriptstyle 1\ \ 1 \end{array}$$ pints (**1 mark**)

Test 8 – pages 16-17

1. a) 10   b) 100   c) 100   d) 1000
   (**2 marks for all four correct,**
   otherwise 1 mark for at least two correct)

2. a) 10   b) 520
   (**1 mark for both answers correct**)

3.
$$\begin{array}{r} 3\ 4 \\ \times\ 1\ 3 \\ \hline 1\ 0_1 2 \\ +\ 3\ 4\ 0 \\ \hline 4\ 4\ 2 \end{array}$$ (**1 mark**) $$\begin{array}{r} 4\ 2 \\ \times\ 2\ 9 \\ \hline 3\ 7_1 8 \\ +\ 8\ 4\ 0 \\ \hline 1\ 2\ 1\ 8 \\ \scriptstyle 1 \end{array}$$ (**1 mark**)

4.
$$\begin{array}{r} 0\ 9\ 1\ 3 \\ 4\overline{)3^3 6\ 5^1 2} \end{array}$$ remainder: 0 (**1 mark**)

$$\begin{array}{r} 1\ 3\ 6\ 7 \\ 6\overline{)8^2 2^4 0^4 4} \end{array}$$ remainder: 2 (**1 mark**)

5.
$$\begin{array}{r} 1\ 5\ 8\ r\ 0 \\ 6\overline{)9^3 4^4 8} \end{array}$$
The remainder is 0, this means that 6 goes into 948 exactly 158 times. True ☑ (**1 mark**)

$$\begin{array}{r} 0\ 7\ 6\ r\ 2 \\ 7\overline{)5^5 3^4 4} \end{array}$$
The remainder is 2, so 7 doesn't divide 534 exactly. This means that 534 isn't a multiple of 7. False ☑ (**1 mark**)

6.
$$\begin{array}{r} 3\ 6 \\ \times\ 2\ 4 \\ \hline 1\ 4_1 4 \\ +\ 7_1 2\ 0 \\ \hline 8\ 6\ 4 \end{array}$$ carrots (**1 mark**)

$$\begin{array}{r} 1\ 8\ 9\ r\ 3 \\ 5\overline{)9^4 4^4 8} \end{array}$$
So the farmer can sell 189 packs.
(**2 marks for the correct answer,**
otherwise 1 mark for a correct method)

Test 9 – pages 18-19

1. a) 36, 48 (**1 mark**)
   b) 45, 60 (**1 mark**)

2. a) 10   b) 30   c) 0   d) 700
   (**2 marks for all four correct,**
   otherwise 1 mark for at least two correct)

3.
$$\begin{array}{r} 0\ 9\ 9\ 5\ r\ 1 \\ 3\overline{)2^2 9^2 8^1 6} \end{array}$$ So the remainder is 1. (**1 mark**)

$$\begin{array}{r} 0\ 8\ 6\ 4\ r\ 3 \\ 4\overline{)3^3 4^2 5^1 9} \end{array}$$ So the remainder is 3. (**1 mark**)

4. 2 × 13 = 26 and 33 − 26 = 7, so 33 ÷ 13 = 2 r 7
   2 × 18 = 36 and 45 − 36 = 9, so 45 ÷ 18 = 2 r 9
   3 × 24 = 72 and 79 − 72 = 7, so 79 ÷ 24 = 3 r 7
   (**2 marks for all three correct,**
   otherwise 1 mark for at least two correct)

5.
$$\begin{array}{r} 6\ 7 \\ \times\ 3\ 2 \\ \hline 1\ 3_{,}4 \\ +\ 2\ 0_{,}1\ 0 \\ \hline 2\ 1\ 4\ 4 \end{array}$$ (**1 mark**) $$\begin{array}{r} 9\ 6 \\ \times\ 5\ 8 \\ \hline 7\ 6_{,}8 \\ +\ 4\ 8_{,}0\ 0 \\ \hline 5\ 5\ 6\ 8 \\ \scriptstyle 1 \end{array}$$ (**1 mark**)

6.
$$\begin{array}{r} 7\ 4 \\ \times\ 2\ 5 \\ \hline 3\ 7_{,}0 \\ +\ 1\ 4\ 8\ 0 \\ \hline 1\ 8\ 5\ 0 \\ \scriptstyle 1 \end{array}$$
25 balloons cost 1850p ÷ 100 = £18.50
So John gets £20 − £18.50 = £1.50 in change.
(**2 marks for the correct answer,**
otherwise 1 mark for a correct method)

Test 10 – pages 20-21

1. a) 5   b) 600   c) 0.24   d) 0.007
   (**2 marks for all four correct,**
   otherwise 1 mark for at least two correct)

2. a) 1   b) 4   c) 7   d) 4
   (**2 marks for all four correct,**
   otherwise 1 mark for at least two correct)

3.
$$\begin{array}{r} 0\ 1\ 1 \\ 14\overline{)1^1 5^1 9} \end{array}$$ remainder: 5 (**1 mark**)

$$\begin{array}{r} 0\ 1\ 2 \\ 26\overline{)3^3 1^5 3} \end{array}$$ remainder: 1 (**1 mark**)

4.
$$\begin{array}{r} 0\ 1\ 3\ r\ 4 \\ 12\overline{)1^1 6^4 0} \end{array}$$
So Wei needs 14 crates.
(**2 marks for the correct answer,**
otherwise 1 mark for a correct method)

5.
$$\begin{array}{r} 1\ 2\ 8 \\ \times\ \ \ 1\ 6 \\ \hline 7_{,}6_{,}8 \\ +\ 1\ 2\ 8\ 0 \\ \hline 2\ 0\ 4\ 8 \\ \scriptstyle 1\ \ 1 \end{array}$$ $$\begin{array}{r} 6\ 4 \\ \times\ \ \ 8 \\ \hline 5\ 1\ 2 \\ \scriptstyle 3 \end{array}$$
So they spelt 2048 + 512 = 2560 words.
(**2 marks for the correct answer,**
otherwise 1 mark for a correct method)

6.
```
      3 3
    × 2 1
    ─────
      3 3
  + 6 6 0
    ─────
    6 9 3  m²
```
**(2 marks for the correct answer,
otherwise 1 mark for a correct method)**

Test 11 – pages 22-23

1. a) 24   b) 30
   (1 mark for both answers correct)

2. a) 80   b) 900   c) 20   d) 10
   **(2 marks for all four correct,
   otherwise 1 mark for at least two correct)**

3.
```
      2 3 8
    ×   5 7
    ───────
    1 6₂6₅6
  + 1 1,9₄0 0
    ───────
    1 3 5 6 6
        1
```
**(2 marks for the correct answer,
otherwise 1 mark for a correct method)**

4.
```
    3 0 1 5              1 6 7 4
  ×     1 2            ×     3 1
  ─────────            ─────────
    6 0 3,0              1 6 7 4
  + 3 0 1 5 0          + 5,0₂2,₁2 0
  ─────────            ─────────
    3 6 1 8 0 (1 mark)   5 1 8 9 4 (1 mark)
```

5.
```
          2 3 4                  3 1 5
    1 2 │2 8 0 8        1 5 │4 7 2 5
        2 4 ▾                  4 5 ▾
        ─────                  ─────
          4 0                    2 2
          3 6 ▾                  1 5 ▾
          ─────                  ─────
            4 8                    7 5
            4 8                    7 5
          ─────                  ─────
              0                      0
```
(1 mark for each correct answer)

6.
```
      3 6 0
    ×   1 2
    ───────
      7,2 0
  + 3 6 0 0
    ───────
    4 3 2 0  cm (1 mark)
      1
```

5640 cm – 4320 cm = 1320 cm
There are 11 gaps between 12 parking spaces.
```
          1 2 0
    1 1 │1 3 2 0
        1 1 ▾
        ─────
          2 2
          2 2
        ─────
            0
```
So each gap has a width of 120 cm.
**(2 marks for the correct answer,
otherwise 1 mark for a correct method)**

Test 12 – pages 24-25

1. a) $4^2 = 4 \times 4 = 16$ b) $9^2 = 9 \times 9 = 81$
   c) $2^3 = 2 \times 2 \times 2 = 8$ d) $3^3 = 3 \times 3 \times 3 = 27$
   **(2 marks for all four correct,
   otherwise 1 mark for at least two correct)**

2. a) 20   b) 40   c) 40   d) 300
   **(2 marks for all four correct,
   otherwise 1 mark for at least two correct)**

3.
```
      9 2 1 8                7 5 4 1
    ×     3 2              ×     9 6
    ─────────              ─────────
    1 8 4 3,6              4 5₃2₂4 6
  + 2 7 6 5,4 0          + 6 7,₄8,₃6 9 0
    ─────────              ─────────
    2 9 4 9 7 6 (1 mark)    7 2 3 9 3 6 (1 mark)
        1                      1 1   1
```

4.
```
            2 2
    1 4 │3 0 8
        2 8 ▾
        ─────
          2 8
          2 8
        ─────
            0
```
So the librarian should place
22 books on each shelf. **(1 mark)**

5.
```
          4 5 2
    1 3 │5 8 7 6
        5 2 ▾
        ─────
          6 7
          6 5 ▾
          ─────
            2 6
            2 6
          ─────
              0  (1 mark)
```

6.
```
          4 1 0
    2 4 │9 8 6 3
        9 6 ▾
        ─────
          2 6
          2 4 ▾
          ─────
            2 3
```
So Mr Boar reads 23 words.
**(2 marks for the correct answer,
otherwise 1 mark for a correct method)**
```
          1 0 3 r 8
    2 4 │2 4 8 0
        2 4 ▾ ▾
        ─────
          0 8 0
            7 2
          ─────
            0 8
```
2480 – 8 = 2472 is a multiple of 24 and
so the book has 2472 words.
**(2 marks for the correct answer,
otherwise 1 mark for a correct method)**

Progress Chart

That's all the tests in the book done — nice one!

Now fill in this table with all of your scores and see how you got on.

	Score
Test 1	
Test 2	
Test 3	
Test 4	
Test 5	
Test 6	
Test 7	
Test 8	
Test 9	
Test 10	
Test 11	
Test 12	

This page may be photocopied

MMDXP21